Dan hurried home to fetch his belongings. "I'm headin' out West to find that gold!" he cried, piling up his luggage. "An' I mustn't forget my favourite object!" Dan gathered all his luggage together, rushed out of the front door, tripped over his favourite object and ended up tied in knots!

TAKE THE INITIAL LETTER OF EACH OF THE ITEMS TO FORM THE NAME OF DAN'S FAVOURITE OBJECT.

WORK OUT THE ORDER OF DAN'S SUITCASES AND BAGS – LARGEST TO SMALLEST. THEN TAKE EACH LETTER IN ORDER AND YOU SHOULD FIND THE NAME OF THE TOWN THAT DAN IS HEADING TOWARDS.

Then Dan made his way to the crowded coach station. Eventually, it was time for Dan's stagecoach to leave. It was a tight squeeze for Dan inside. "Prickly porcupine!" he grumbled, squashing himself onto a seat. "This just ain't my idea of fun!"

WHAT IS A COW'S FAVOURITE STAGE SHOW?

A MOO-SICAL!

USE A MIRROR TO FIND OUT THE HOLIDAY DESTINATIONS OF THESE LUGGAGE LABELS.

SPAIN

NORWAY

ITALY

FRANCE

SCOTLAND

AFRICA

INDIA

AUSTRALIA

THE NUMBERED PASSENGERS ARE ALL GOING ON DIFFERENT TYPES OF ACTIVITY HOLIDAY. LOOK AT THEIR OUTFITS AND GUESS WHO IS GOING WHERE.

Dan stared out of the stagecoach window, watching the incredible scenery go by. He was just dozing off when a loud whooping and hollering startled him. "Why, it's the no-good Blackfoot Tribe!" exclaimed Dan, climbing up to sit beside the driver. "Are they called 'Blackfoot' 'cause they never wash their feet?" joked the driver.

WHAT DO YOU GET IF YOU CROSS A COWBOY'S HEADGEAR WITH A SHIP?

A TEN-GALLEON HAT!

LOOK AT THE PICTURE CLUES AND SEE IF YOU CAN WORK OUT WHAT AMAZING THINGS THE STAGECOACH PASSED.

ALL OF THE INDIANS' HEADDRESSES ARE THE SAME APART FROM ONE. CAN YOU FIND IT?

Before you could say 'slithering sidewinders' the Indians quickly surrounded the stagecoach. "We'd best surrender," muttered Dan, crossly. "Ain't no good fightin' in case the passengers get hurt!" The Indians took Dan and the rest of the passengers back to their camp and tied them to a totem pole. Then the Indians started to dance around them.

"Ha! Call that dancin'?" laughed Dan.

COUNT THE NUMBER OF FEATHERS TO FIND OUT HOW MANY INDIANS HAVE SURROUNDED THE STAGECOACH.

HOW MANY COMPLETE TRIANGLES CAN YOU FIND IN THE TOTEM POLE AND TEPEES?

"Grrr! We give um big man big torture!" boomed the Indian Chief. He pulled a long feather from his headdress and tickled Dan. "Hee hee! Ha ha!" Dan chortled. "I'm in a real ticklish situation. I've gotta get outta here!" Dan tore the totem pole out of the ground and tripped up the Indians. While they ran to their Medicine Man for bandages, Dan untied everyone's hands. "Let's escape!" he called.

WORK OUT THE NAMES OF THE INDIANS FROM THESE CLUES.

① ✗IG CH∧EF

②

③

④

⑤ CR ✗AZY

⑥ L ✗

⑦

WALKS _ _ _ _ _ A _ _ _ _ _ _ _

Dan and the passengers hurried away into the desert. "You saved our lives!" cried the driver. "But we'll never reach Deadman Town without the stagecoach – we're bound to dry up in this burning sun!" "No problem!" said Dan. And with that, he produced several cow-pies from his bag. "Hooray!" cried the passengers, as they tucked into the meal.

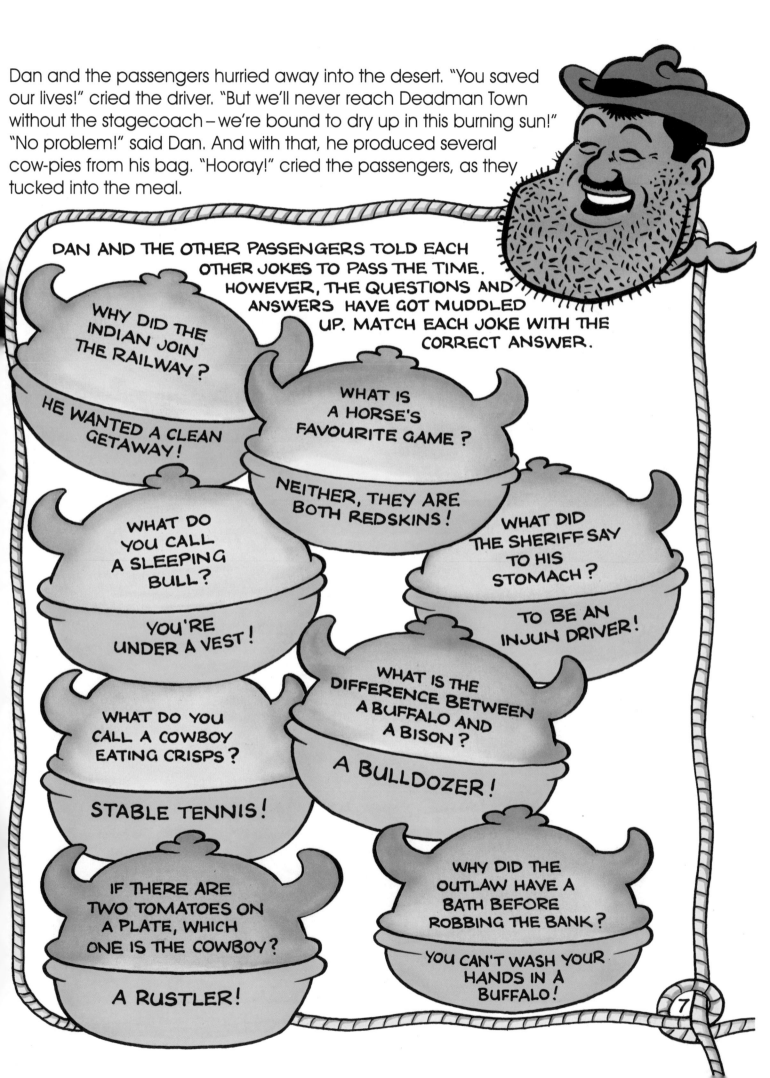

DAN AND THE OTHER PASSENGERS TOLD EACH OTHER JOKES TO PASS THE TIME. HOWEVER, THE QUESTIONS AND ANSWERS HAVE GOT MUDDLED UP. MATCH EACH JOKE WITH THE CORRECT ANSWER.

WHY DID THE INDIAN JOIN THE RAILWAY?

HE WANTED A CLEAN GETAWAY!

WHAT IS A HORSE'S FAVOURITE GAME?

NEITHER, THEY ARE BOTH REDSKINS!

WHAT DO YOU CALL A SLEEPING BULL?

YOU'RE UNDER A VEST!

WHAT DID THE SHERIFF SAY TO HIS STOMACH?

TO BE AN INJUN DRIVER!

WHAT DO YOU CALL A COWBOY EATING CRISPS?

STABLE TENNIS!

WHAT IS THE DIFFERENCE BETWEEN A BUFFALO AND A BISON?

A BULLDOZER!

IF THERE ARE TWO TOMATOES ON A PLATE, WHICH ONE IS THE COWBOY?

A RUSTLER!

WHY DID THE OUTLAW HAVE A BATH BEFORE ROBBING THE BANK?

YOU CAN'T WASH YOUR HANDS IN A BUFFALO!

After many hours of trekking across the desert, Dan and the passengers finally reached Deadman Town, said their goodbyes and went their separate ways.

SEE IF YOU CAN WORK OUT HOW LONG IT TOOK DAN AND THE OTHER PASSENGERS TO REACH DEADMAN TOWN.

ONE WHOLE PIE = 1 HOUR

HALF A PIE = $\frac{1}{2}$ HOUR

QUARTER OF A PIE = $\frac{1}{4}$ HOUR

BLACKFOOT CAMP

DEADMAN TOWN

Make your own Desperate Dan

To make your very own Desperate Dan, carefully cut out the card pieces. Match the letters to get the pieces in the right place, using brass paper fasteners to join them together.

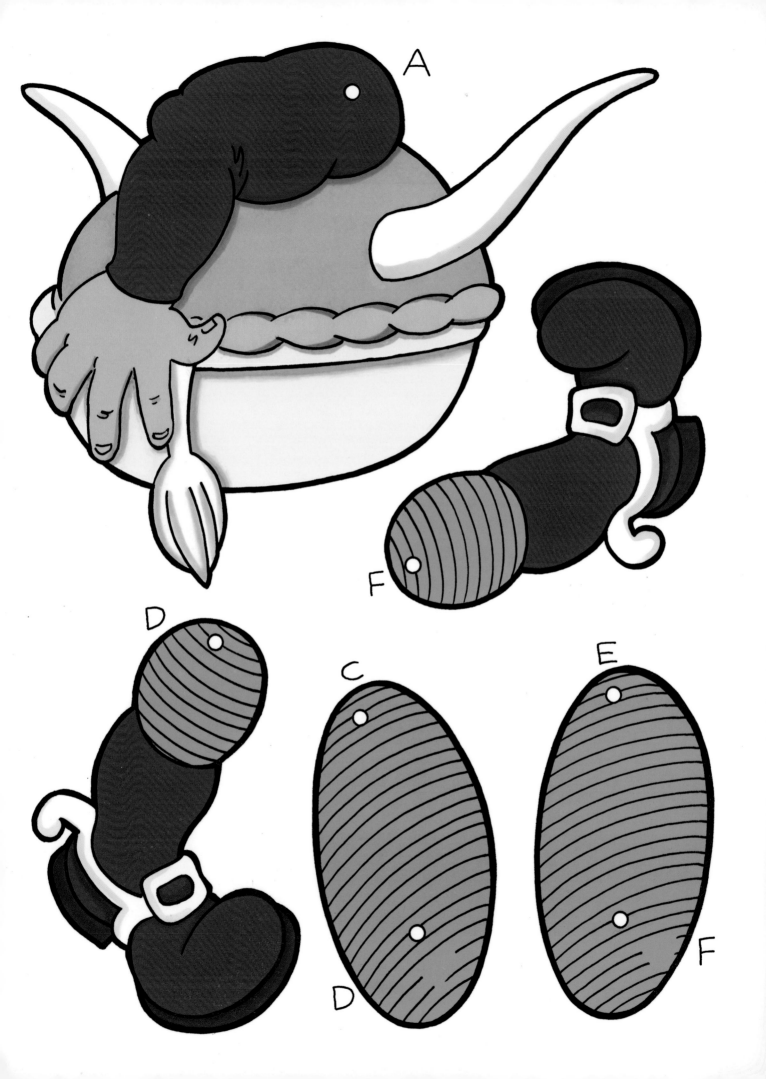

As Dan headed quickly down the town's high street, the shops shook and great clouds of dust billowed up behind him. The Town Sheriff peeked out from the barber's window. "I thought we were in for a thunderstorm!" he gasped, seeing Dan march noisily by.

THE SHOP SIGNS HAVE BEEN SHAKEN UP. CAN YOU SORT THEM OUT?

DRAW A LINE TO MATCH THESE OBJECTS WITH THE CORRECT SIGNS.

ARBREB
KREAB
NABK
LEOTH
RGORCE
EACF
OSPT FOFEIC
MICHSTE

"I can hear thunder, too!" thought Dan. He turned round and found himself in the path of a herd of stampeding bulls. Quick as a flash, he hurled his lasso, twirling it over the head of the leading bull. Then he leaped onto its back and rode it into the nearest field.

WHAT DID THE SICK LASSO SAY?

I'M FEELING A BIT ROPEY!

WORK OUT WHICH COWBOY HAS LASSOED WHICH ANIMAL.

Having safely penned in the rest of the bulls, Dan left the town and continued to follow the trail on the map. He eventually found himself in the mountains. "I can smell gold from here!" he thought as he climbed up the mountain. At the top, there was an entrance that led to a maze of caves. "But which route to take?" he wondered.

Desperate Dan flexed his muscles and, with a great heave, he lifted the lid to reveal the most dazzling trove of gold ever found. Dan was delighted! He tucked the treasure chest under his arm and set off down the mountain towards home.

HELP DESPERATE DAN TO GET HIS GOLD BACK HOME BY CHANGING THE WORD GOLD TO HOME IN TWO MOVES, CHANGING ONLY ONE LETTER.

DAN HAS DECIDED TO SHARE OUT HIS FIND WITH HIS FRIENDS. HE WILL VISIT EVERYBODY, BUT ONLY ONCE, AND IN THE ORDER OF THE DOOR NUMBERS, MOVING IN ANY DIRECTION EXCEPT DIAGONALLY. SEE IF YOU CAN WORK OUT THE ROUTE THAT HE TOOK.

  (13)   (23)

START

HOME

(4)   (8)    (27)

13

Dan decided to invite all the town folk to a big party to celebrate finding the treasure. "Where's the rest of the gold then?" asked Danny and Katey, hoping for some more pocket money.
Dan smiled. "Gold? I've already spent it!"

CAN YOU FIND TEN DIFFERENCES BETWEEN THESE TWO PARTY PICTURES?

Aunt Aggie was aghast. "What have you bought that would cost so much?" she demanded. Dan pulled away a sheet that was hiding a large object in his garden. To everyone's amazement there stood before them the most enormous cow-pie that they had ever seen. "Tuck in, everyone!" Dan chuckled.

JOIN THE DOTS TO SEE DAN'S SURPRISE !

Answers

Page 1   Cat E
7 hats
The map should read:

TREASURE CHEST OF GOLD CAN BE FOUND IN THE WILD WEST

Page 2   LASSO
DEADMAN TOWN

Page 3   Holiday luggage labels, top, left to right: SPAIN, NORWAY, ITALY, FRANCE
bottom, left to right: SCOTLAND, AFRICA, INDIA, AUSTRALIA
Holiday activities: **1)** seaside; **2)** camping; **3)** dancing; **4)** surfing; **5)** climbing; **6)** snorkelling

Page 4   **1)** a bald man walking past a wall; **2)** a stork with a wooden leg; **3)** a deer lying down;
4) a Mexican frying an egg; **5)** a bear yawning; **6)** a bear climbing a tree;
7) a cowboy's hairy arm; **8)** an arrow flying towards you!
Indian B

Page 5   28 feathers
41 triangles

Page 6   **1)** Big Chief Sitting Tortoise; **2)** Little Rabbit; **3)** Snake in the Grass; **4)** Running Nose;
5) Crazy Mouse; **6)** Walks like a Chicken; **7)** Fish Face

Page 7   **Q:** Why did the Indian join the railway?   **A:** To be an injun driver!
Q: What is a horse's favourite game?   **A:** Stable tennis!
Q: What do you call a sleeping bull?   **A:** A bulldozer!
Q: What did the sheriff say to his stomach?   **A:** You're under a vest!
Q: What do you call a cowboy eating crisps?   **A:** A rustler!
Q: What is the difference between a buffalo and a bison?
A: You can't wash your hands in a buffalo!
Q: If there are two tomatoes on a plate, which one is the cowboy?
A: Neither, they are both redskins!
Q: Why did the outlaw have a bath before robbing the bank?   **A:** He wanted a clean getaway!

Page 8   11 hours

Page 9   Left to right: BARBER; CHEMIST; BAKER; HOTEL; CAFE; POST OFFICE; BANK; GROCER
BARBER – scissors; BAKER – bread; BANK – money; HOTEL – bed; GROCER – carrot/apple;
CAFE – coffee cup; POST OFFICE – stamp; CHEMIST – medicine bottle

Page 10   **1)** bull; **2)** rabbit; **3)** cat; **4)** dog; **5)** horse

Page 12   No. If you thought key 5, look again. Dan will have to rip open the chest.

Page 13   GOLD
|
HOLD
|
HOLE
|
HOME

Page 14   Indian feather; Indian's loincloth pattern; missing balloon; Dan's necktie; cowboy's hatband;
Dan's spur; fringe on cowgirl's arm; Katey's right pigtail; Danny's buttons; Danny's hat feather

CONTENTS

Words printed in **bold** appear in the glossary.

GETTING STARTED

Think of the everyday things that are made of clay: the bricks and tiles for building houses; the plates and cups we eat and drink from. Clay is also used by artists and craftspeople to make models, **sculptures** and decorative objects. Objects made from clay are called 'pottery'.

Clay is a very useful natural material that is dug out of the earth. Clay was formed many millions of years ago. Over hundreds of centuries, frost, wind, rain and heat from the sun worked away at the rocks of the earth's surface, wearing down some areas to tiny sticky grains of clay. Clay can be many different colours, depending on the different **minerals** contained in the original rocks. For example, clay with iron in it is a reddish-brown or yellowish-orange colour.

▼ *This man is adding water to clay and pounding it with his feet to make it softer and easier to model.*

When clay is first dug out of the ground it is soft and wet, so it is easy to model. In the air, the water in the clay starts to **evaporate**. The clay dries out and becomes lighter in colour. It can no longer be modelled. If the clay is then heated to a high temperature – in a bonfire or a **kiln** – all the water is driven out of it and it changes again. It becomes extremely hard. This process is called **firing**.

Clay appears in these three different forms because it is made up of flat, **hexagonal**-shaped **particles**. When clay is wet, there is water between the particles, and so they can slip and slide about. As the clay becomes drier, there is nothing for the particles to slide on. When the clay is heated, the particles **fuse** together.

There are three main ways of shaping clay; using a **potter's wheel**, a **mould** made of **plaster** or your hands. This book looks especially at ways of shaping clay by hand. The same ideas can be used with other modelling materials – cold clays and Plasticine, which can be bought from shops, or home-made play dough and salt dough.

Arts & Crafts

MODELLING

With

Wayland

Titles in this series

BATIK AND TIE-DYE
BLOCK PRINTING
KNITTING AND CROCHET
MODELLING
NEEDLECRAFT
PAPER MAKING
STENCILS AND SCREENS
WEAVING

Frontispiece *A model of modelling!
This little figure, from Venezuela,
shows a woman making a coil pot.*

This edition published in 1994
by Wayland (Publishers) Ltd

© Copyright 1993 Wayland
(Publishers) Ltd

First published in 1993 by
Wayland (Publishers) Ltd
61 Western Road, Hove
East Sussex BN3 1JD, England

Editor: Anna Girling
Designer: Jean Wheeler

**British Library Cataloguing in
Publication Data**
O'Reilly, Susie
Modelling. – (Arts & Crafts Series)
I. Title II. Series
731.4

HARDBACK ISBN 0-7502-0711-6

PAPERBACK ISBN 0-7502-1375-2

Typeset by Dorchester Typesetting
Group Ltd, Dorchester, Dorset, England
Printed and bound by Lego, Italy

▲ *The ancient Greeks made models of everyday scenes. Try making your own, like this.*

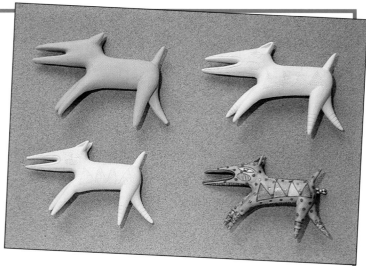

▲ *These pottery brooches show clay at four different stages: (top row) wet; dry but not fired; (bottom row) fired; decorated and fired again.*

TOOLS AND MATERIALS

To get started you will need the following equipment.

Materials:
clay (bought or from a garden); fine sand for adding to garden clay; Plasticine; cold clays (e.g. Fimo).

General equipment:
overall; wooden board (unvarnished) or piece of sacking cloth to work on; polythene sheets, plastic bags and airtight containers; old toothbrush; old table knife; rolling pin; spray bottle; paper and pencils; squared paper.

Modelling tools:
e.g. lollypop sticks; old screwdriver; comb.

Scraping and smoothing tools:
e.g. sponge; seashells; wooden ruler or spoon.

Decorating tools:
e.g. plastic cutlery; pastry cutters; darning needle; old Biro; nails; screws; buttons; leaves; twigs; fir cones; pebbles; string; bottle-tops; sieve or garlic crusher.

For making dough:
flour; salt; wallpaper paste powder; powder paint; food colouring; cream of tartar; cooking oil; plastic bowl; baking tray.

For finishing off:
poster paints; varnish; PVA glue.

For clearing up:
scraper; broom; dustpan and brush; sponge.

Safety
Be careful not to create clay dust – breathing it in can be harmful. Do not scrape dried clay with sandpaper. Clear up small pieces of clay using a damp cloth. Wipe work areas with a damp sponge. Avoid brushing as much as possible.

If you get clay on your clothing, wait for it to dry completely and then brush it off.

Do not wash clay down the sink. It will block the drains.

THE HISTORY OF MODELLING

We know that people have been making clay pots, for cooking and storing food, for at least 8,000 years. However, even 100,000 years before that, clay was being used to make models of people and animals. These models were probably thought to keep away evil spirits and to bring good luck.

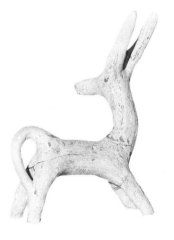

◄ *This ancient animal figure is probably a deer. It was found on the island of Crete and was made about 4,000 years ago.*

Among the early peoples of North and South America there were highly skilled potters. Archaeologists have found coiled, moulded and modelled pots, decorated with clever designs. For example, there are cooking pots decorated with modelled faces. The faces look upwards, so they can be seen by people looking down on the pot from above.

It seems that early people took great care when choosing and preparing their clay. Sometimes they would travel some distance to collect special clay, or they would add sand or ash so that delicate figures could be modelled and fired without the clay cracking.

Clay objects provide useful information about the world's earliest peoples. Clay that has been fired may shatter, but it does not rot away like wood or fabric, so **archaeologists** have been able to stick pieces of pottery back together. Many clay objects have been found in ancient graves. People were often buried with cooking pots, jewellery, toys and other items. They thought they might need them in their next life.

◄ *A Peruvian pot, with a handle and spout, made in the shape of a jaguar (a big cat). It is over 1,000 years old.*

A model of a ► *man kneeling, made in Japan in the seventh century.*

The ancient Egyptians, Greeks and Romans made clay models of everyday scenes. For example, there are models of people taking baths, going to market, playing musical instruments and acting in plays. These models were often made as toys or perfume bottles.

This ancient ▶ bowl comes from what is now Egypt. The inside has been rubbed to make it shiny.

▲ *A scene from everyday life: this ancient Greek model shows a man sawing wood.*

▼ *An army of life-size soldiers, guarding an ancient tomb in Xian, China.*

Throughout history, the Chinese have been famous for their pottery skills. Much early Chinese pottery has been found in **tombs**. During times of war, whole armies of soldiers, sometimes life-size, were modelled, painted in brilliant colours and buried in the tombs of important people. It was believed that they would protect them from enemies.

▼ *In Nigeria, in Africa, over 2,000 years ago, people made models of human heads.*

MODERN MODELLING

In some parts of the world today, for example in South America and Africa, people are still making pottery using the same coiling, moulding and modelling techniques used by their **ancestors** hundreds, and even thousands, of years ago.

▲ American potter Richard Zane Smith uses extremely thin coils to build large pots. He leaves the coils showing as part of the design. (Photo: courtesy of Gallery 10, Scottsdale and Santa Fe)

◄ In Mexico, even large pots are made by hand.

▼ A potter from Tanzania, East Africa, smooths the surface of a hand-modelled pot.

However, in **developed countries**, most clay goods – pipes, bricks, tiles and crockery – are made in factories. In the eighteenth and nineteenth centuries the **Industrial Revolution** brought great changes to western Europe and the United States. Huge machines and factories were built to produce cheap goods in large amounts. It seemed that potters who worked by hand were no longer needed.

In the twentieth century, though, artists and craftspeople have again become interested in hand-modelled pottery. They have studied hand-modelling techniques from around the world. Today in many developed countries, especially Britain, Japan, the United States and Canada, young people train at college to work with clay. Craftspeople are able to make a living from their work, making modelled sculptures and wonderful pots.

Clay can be ▶ *modelled to make jewellery. This teapot ear-ring was made by Californian Jaye Lawrence.*

A pot by ▶ *Bernard Leach, a famous British potter. Leach went to live in Japan in 1909, and learnt how the Japanese made pots. Many European potters were influenced by his work.*

Many modern potters work using a wheel, but others hand-build, using a mixture of pinching, coiling and slabbing techniques. Although they are using the same methods as potters have used for thousands of years, they also make full use of all the technical and scientific information available today. They are very fussy about the clay they use. They search carefully to find clay that will behave just as they want.

◀ *This clown brooch was hand-made by Trish Rafferty.*

Kate Malone takes ideas from nature for her ▶ *work. Does this jug remind you of a pumpkin?*

PREPARING THE CLAY

Clay can be bought from suppliers of art and craft materials. Bought modelling clay usually comes in one of two colours. Red clay gets its colour from the iron it contains. It is warm and earthy and feels good. It can stain your hands and equipment. Grey clay does not stain but it leaves more dust. It is easier to paint.

Bought modelling clay sometimes has pieces of fired clay or sawdust added to it. This gives it more body and makes it easier to work. It also helps the clay to hold any shape it is modelled into.

If your home has a garden with a clay soil, you may be able to dig up your own clay. Never do this without asking an adult first. Both bought and garden clays need to be prepared before you can start modelling.

PREPARING BOUGHT CLAY

1 The clay will be sold in a plastic bag. Before you start, you need to check its **consistency**. It should be not too dry and not too wet. Hold a small ball in your hand and squeeze it with your fingers. It should feel soft, and stay in the shape you squeeze.

◀ *Three types of common clay: (from left) grey; red; with fired clay added.*

2 If the clay cracks easily, it is too dry to work with. Make it into small balls, the size of your fist. Push your thumbs into the centre of the balls. Fill them with water and place inside a polythene bag for a day or two. The clay will take in the water and become soft enough to model.

10

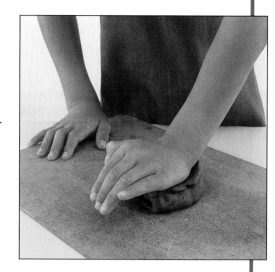

its ends, and leave for a day. The air can get all round the clay and it will dry out.

4 Clay is usually full of air bubbles. If it is heated in a kiln, the air bubbles will **expand** and shatter the clay. **Kneading** the clay gets rid of the air bubbles, and also makes it easier to model.

3 If the clay sticks to your fingers, it is too wet. Roll it into a thick sausage. Bend it over so that it stands on

Put a lump of clay on an unvarnished board or some sacking (to stop it sticking

to the table). Use the heel of your palm to keep pushing the clay away from you. It helps to stand up.

PREPARING GARDEN CLAY

1 Ask an adult to help you find an area of clay soil and dig out a lump of it.

2 Pick out all stones, twigs and leaves mixed up in the clay.

3 If it is sticky, mix in some fine sand. You will need about two parts of sand to three parts of clay. This will make it easier to model and help it to stay in shape.

4 Now knead the clay in the same way as for bought clay.

Remember: clay, cold clay, play dough and salt dough dry out quickly. If you want to reuse clay or dough, or if you want to continue working on a model on another day, wrap it in polythene or put it in an airtight container.

PINCHING

The simplest way to start modelling is by pinching, pulling and squeezing. You can use clay, salt dough, play dough, Plasticine and cold clays. Make models of animals, people or plants. Or make all kinds of pots – broad and low, tall and thin, large, small, bulky or delicate. It's up to you!

MAKING A MODEL

▼ *Try making models using Plasticine of various colours.*

1 Take a piece of clay or dough. With your hands, start to pinch and squeeze the lump into the shape of a bird, an animal, a person or a plant.

2 As you pull and push the clay or dough, it may begin to suggest a new shape to you. Help this new idea along. Give the shape more features by adding extra pieces.

3 Try using some of your modelling tools to add details and decoration.

MAKING PINCH POTS

1 Take a lump of clay that fits into the palm of your hand. Roll it into a smooth ball between your palms.

2 Hold the lump in one hand and press the thumb of your other hand into the middle of the ball, making a deep hole.

3 Keep the ball cupped in your hand and pinch out the clay between your thumb and fingers. Keep turning the ball of clay round in your hand, and carefully pull out the walls. Slowly pinch them out so that they become thinner and thinner.

4 After a while the walls will become floppy. Put the pot to one side, standing it upside-down on its rim. Leave it for about an hour.

5 When the clay has stiffened up, carry on pinching out the shape.

VARIATIONS

1 Add a coil to the top to make a rim. Pinch out the rim to make it look like the edge of a pie.

2 Add a coil to the base of the pot to make a foot. See pages 14-15 for instructions on making coils.

3 You can also model feet to add to the base of the pot.

MAKING COIL POTS

Using coils of clay is a way of building up shapes, layer by layer. The shape grows gradually, so you can think carefully about how things are working out as you go along – and make changes if you want to. Tiny pots and huge pots, even pots as large as a person, can be made with coils. In Nigeria, in West Africa, potters even use clay coils to build houses.

1 Break off a piece of clay. Roll it between your hands to make a sausage shape.

2 Place the sausage on a wooden board and roll it using both your hands. Keep rolling until it is about as fat as a felt-tipped pen. Make about six rolls, all the same thickness.

3 Roll out a piece of clay with a rolling pin. Use a lid from a jar or tin to cut out the base for a pot.

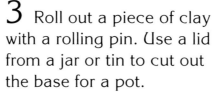

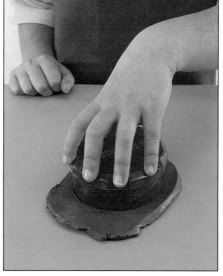

4 Place a coil on the top of the base, running it round the outside edge. Smooth it firmly on to the base, on the inside, using your thumb or a modelling tool.

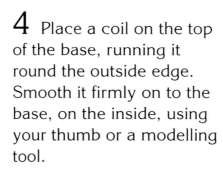

5 When you have worked all round the base, break off any extra coil. Use your fingers to smooth the ends together.

6 Now add a second coil. As you add more and more coils, make sure you place the joins in different places. Support the wall of the pot with one hand and smooth the inside with the fingers of your other hand.

TURN TO PAGE 5 FOR A LIST OF TOOLS TO USE.

7 To make the pot get fatter, place each coil on the outside edge of the one before. To make it get thinner, place each coil on the inside edge.

8 Once you are pleased with the size and shape of the pot, smooth over all the outside coils. Use the tools you have collected to beat, scrape or smooth the pot.

VARIATIONS

1 To get a really smooth surface, let the pot dry until it is just damp. Then rub it with the back of a metal spoon or a round pebble. This is called **burnishing**.

2 Pinch and squeeze the clay on the side of the pot to make a raised pattern. Add pieces of clay or modelled figures.

3 Use some of your decorating tools to press a pattern into the clay. Or leave the coils showing on the outside as a decorative feature.

MAKING SLAB POTS

Slabs are used to make straight-sided pots and models. You can make containers, or model houses, boats and bridges. If you are making a very regular shape, it helps to make a paper **template** to use as a pattern from which the parts can be cut. Slabs can also be made into attractive tiles. You can scratch a pattern or design into the surface, or add pieces of clay to make a raised decoration.

USING FIRM CLAY

◀ *Try using slabs to make model buildings out of Plasticine.*

1 Decide what you are going to make – perhaps a box or a model house – and work out the **measurements** for the slabs you will need. On squared paper, make templates for the pieces.

2 Using a rolling pin, roll a piece of clay out flat on a board or piece of sacking. To get an even surface, roll the clay between two strips of wood, about 1 cm thick.

3 Put your templates on the clay and cut out the shapes, using a knife.

4 Roughen the edges of the slabs, so that they grip each other firmly when they are joined.

5 If you are using clay, dampen the edges with a wet brush so that it becomes sticky. If you are using Plasticine or play dough, you do not need to dampen the edges.

USING SOFT CLAY

1 Roll out a sheet of clay on a piece of cloth. Wrap it around a tube – perhaps an old plastic bottle, or the inner tube from a roll of paper towel.

6 Join the pieces together, smoothing the joins firmly with your fingers.

4 Cut out a base from another slab. Roughen and dampen the edges. Join the base to the tube.

5 Change the shape of the pot – pinch the sides or add extra clay. Or cut away pieces of the pot, to make a pattern of holes.

2 Cut the clay so that the edges meet and smooth over the join.

7 For extra strength, roll out very thin ropes of clay and press them into each join, on the inside.

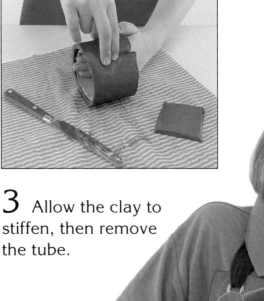

3 Allow the clay to stiffen, then remove the tube.

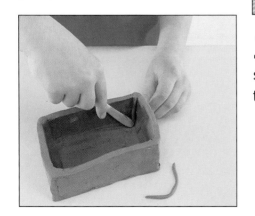

SALT DOUGH

Salt dough is easy to make. Salt dough models will last for many years if they are properly dried and varnished. **Remember: salt dough may look like pastry, but it cannot be eaten**.

MAKING SALT DOUGH

You will need:

75 g of flour
150 g of salt
1/2 teaspoon of
   wallpaper
   paste powder
50 ml of water
3 teaspoons of
   powder paint

1 Mix the salt, flour, powder paint and wallpaper paste powder in an old plastic bowl.

2 Add water to the salt mixture and stir well to make a firm dough.

3 Knead the dough, using the heel of your palm (see page 11). This will mix the ingredients together thoroughly.

4 Put the dough in a plastic bag, tie up the top and leave it in a refrigerator overnight.

5 Use other powder paints to make doughs in a number of different colours.

5 To stick on the decorations, dampen the backs using a brush that has been dipped in water.

MAKING TREE DECORATIONS

1 Make templates of shapes to cut round. Try: stars, boots, faces, birds, aeroplanes, or anything you like.

2 Take your dough out of the refrigerator. Put some flour on a wooden board (so that the dough does not stick) and roll out the dough with a rolling pin.

3 Put the templates on the dough and cut round them with a knife.

4 Decorate your shapes with pieces of different-coloured dough. To do this, roll out a thin slab of dough. Press out small shapes using pastry cutters, old Biros or bottle tops. Experiment and have fun.

6 Make a small hole at the top of each shape, so that you will be able to thread through some string and hang them up.

7 Put the shapes on a baking tray. Ask an adult to put the tray in an oven set at 110 °C or gas mark *slow/economy*. Leave for six hours. When they are dry, varnish first one side and then the other.

PLAY DOUGH

Play dough can be pinched, squeezed, rolled into slabs and coiled – just like clay. If you keep it in an airtight container, you can use the same dough over and over again.

MAKING PLAY DOUGH

1 Weigh the ingredients carefully and mix them together in a bowl.

2 Put the mixture in a saucepan and heat it on a cooker over a low heat. **Ask an adult to help you do this**. Stir all the time until the mixture turns into a ball. Turn off the heat.

3 When the dough has cooled, knead it thoroughly (see page 11).

4 Make dough in a range of different colours.

You will need:

150 g of flour
60 g of salt
110 ml of water

1 tablespoon of cooking oil
3 teaspoons of cream
   of tartar
1 teaspoon of food
   colouring or powder paint

PLAY DOUGH MODELS

1 Make a living room scene. Roll out a slab of play dough. Add play dough in other colours to make a patterned mat.

2 Pinch out the body and head of a cat. Stick on extra play dough for the tail and feet.

3 Use play dough in different colours to model a person in an armchair.

Think of other scenes to model: a circus, a fair, a visit to the zoo, an afternoon at the beach, or a football match. Ask some friends to work with you.

MODELLING A PORTRAIT HEAD

Look very carefully at people's heads. Make some big, bold drawings of several people, using a soft pencil. Notice that each person's head is a very different shape. The way the features (eyes, nose, lips, ears, hair) fit together varies from person to person. Make drawings of the back, front and side of a person's head. Try closing your eyes and gently feeling a friend's face.

1 Cut off a large piece of soft, but not sticky, clay. Put it on a board.

2 Model the clay into the basic shape of the head, neck and shoulders.

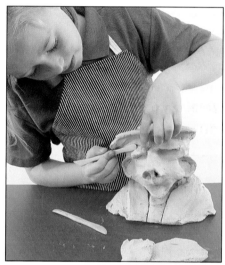

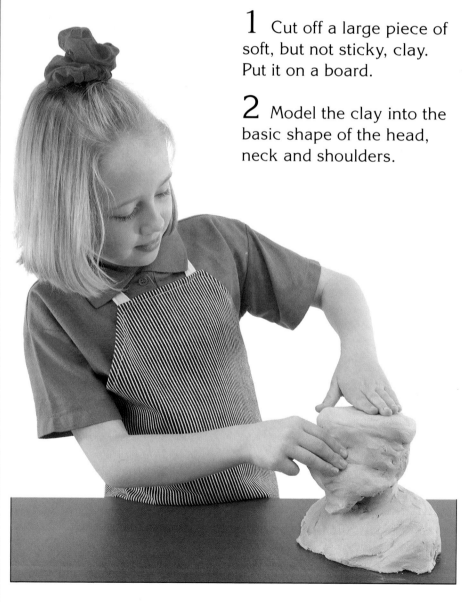

3 Pull, pinch and squeeze out the eyes, eyebrows, ears, nose and lips. Add extra pieces of clay if necessary.

4 Try to remember that your model is **three-dimensional.** Turn the head round to work on the sides and the back. Really good models are as interesting from the back and side as from the front.

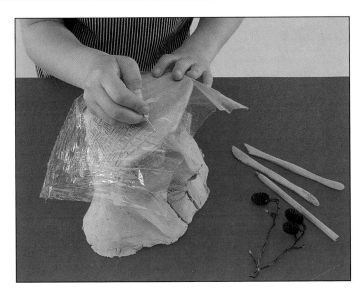

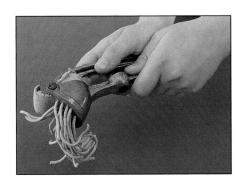

7 To make hair, press some clay through a sieve or a garlic crusher.

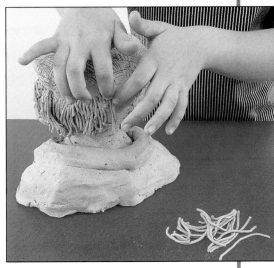

5 To model fine details, put a piece of polythene over the area and use the end of a darning needle to press or draw in the marks you want.

8 When you are pleased with your model, leave the head to dry out for a day. Then scratch in some fine details – laughter lines round the eyes, or hairs.

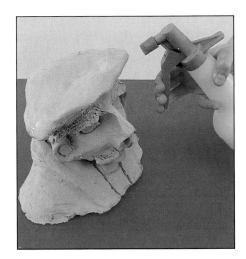

TURN TO PAGES **26-7** FOR IDEAS ON FINISHING OFF YOUR MODEL.

6 If the clay begins to dry out, spray water on it using a spray bottle (the sort used to spray houseplants). If you need to stop work, cover the clay carefully with a polythene sheet to stop it drying out.

MAKING A WALL PLAQUE

When you have learnt the basic methods of pinching, coils and slabs there is no end to the things you can model. Invent ways of combining these methods. Let your imagination go wild. Use your eyes, a notebook and a camera to look for things that suggest ideas. The idea for this wall plaque is a rock pool, but you could do something quite different. For example, make a plaque to illustrate a story. Or make several plaques telling different parts of a story.

1 Roll out a slab of clay and cut it into the shape you want. As this plaque is about a rock pool, you could choose the shape of a crab or a starfish.

2 Make two holes in the top of the plaque so that you can attach string to hang it on a wall.

3 Make other shapes and stick them on to the base slab. Decide whether you want them to lie flat on the base, or stand out.

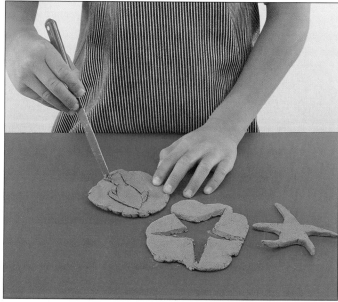

24

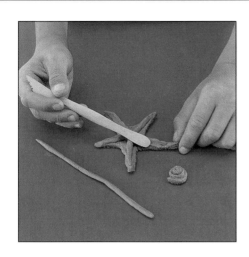

4 Make balls, rolls and coils of clay to add to the basic shapes. Use your tools to press patterns into the clay. Remember: to make sure the clay dries out evenly, do not let any parts get too thick. This is especially important if you are going to fire it.

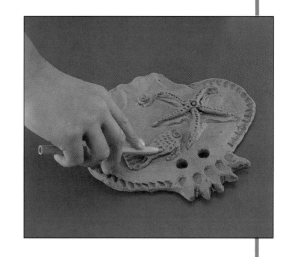

5 When you have finished modelling, allow your plaque to dry out. Then decorate it with paint and varnish.

6 Thread a piece of ribbon or string through the holes in the top of the plaque to hang it on the wall.

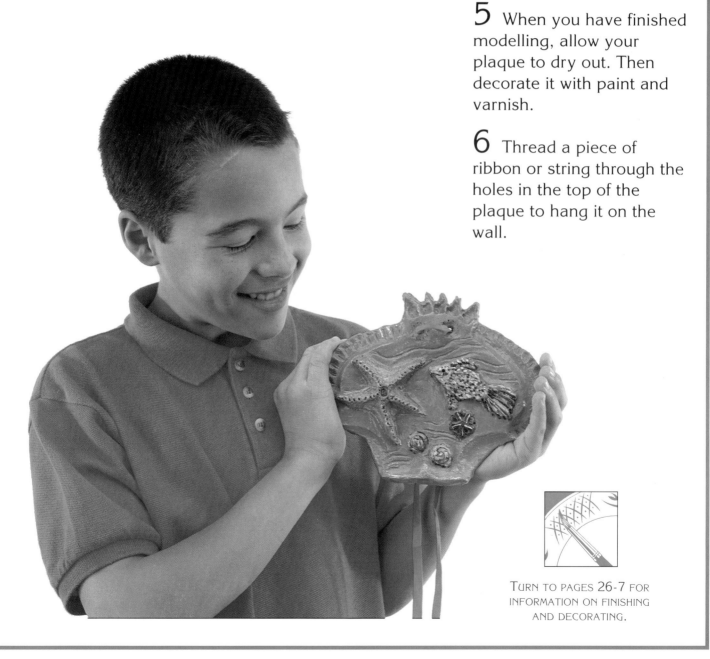

TURN TO PAGES 26-7 FOR INFORMATION ON FINISHING AND DECORATING.

FINISHING AND DECORATING

Sometimes you may just want to have fun modelling and using materials. Sometimes, however, you may want to keep the pots and models you make. There are a number of ways you can do this.

Clay can be fired in a kiln and then decorated with **glazes**. This involves special equipment and you will need a grown-up to help you. But there are other things you can do for yourself.

Salt dough and cold clays can be dried out thoroughly in a cool oven (six hours at about 110 °C or gas mark slow/economy). **Ask an adult to help you do this**. When the pieces are dry they can be painted and varnished. Some cold clays come in bright colours and do not need to be painted.

▲ This plant pot holder has been fired but not glazed.

This model ▶ rock pool was fired, decorated with coloured glazes and fired again.

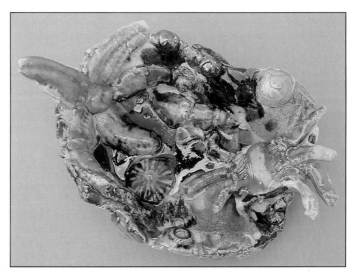

PAINTING AND VARNISHING CLAY MODELS

1 Let the clay dry out completely. This will take several days.

2 Add water to PVA glue and paint this mixture all over the model. This will help to make the dry clay less crumbly and fragile.

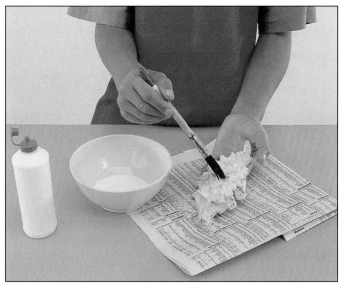

4 Paint the basic colour of your model all over. Then add details in different colours. Use poster paints which are thick enough to use one on top of another, without the colours showing through.

5 When it is dry give the model two coats of varnish to protect it.

3 Paint the model with a coat of white paint to give a good background to work on.

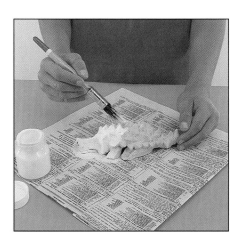

THE GALLERY

It is very important to understand that modelling is all about making things that have three dimensions. This means making things that can be looked at from the front, from the side and from the back. When you are looking for ideas for modelling, try to find things that have three dimensions too.

Try drawing objects from different viewpoints. Take a big sheet of paper and a soft pencil, and make several big, bold drawings of the same object. If you discover that the back and the side view are uninteresting, choose something else to model.

▲ *Smooth pebbles.*

Try closing your eyes and handling some shells, stones or pieces of pottery. You will be surprised at the range of different feelings you can get from the surface of an object. Think of words that describe the **textures**: rough, smooth, grainy, crumbly, spiky. These pictures will give you some ideas for things to look out for.

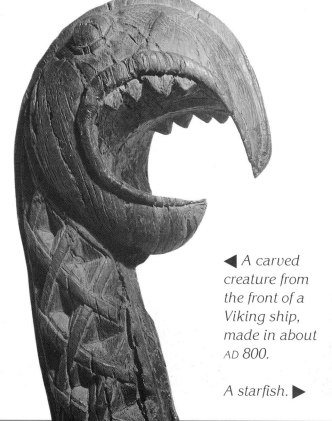

◄ *A carved creature from the front of a Viking ship, made in about AD 800.*

A starfish. ▶

▲ *A sitting horse.*

◄ *A sculpture by Henry Moore.*

▼ *Rugged mountains that look like a monster's back.*

◄ *A prickly cactus.*

► *Your pet cat.*

▼ *Round pumpkins.*

GLOSSARY

Ancestors Members of a family who lived long ago.

Archaeologists People who find out what happened in the past by studying ancient remains.

Burnishing Polishing a surface by rubbing it to make it extremely smooth.

Consistency The thickness or firmness of something.

Developed countries Countries which have complicated systems for industry, transport and finance. In developing countries, on the other hand, people rely on small-scale farming and crafts.

Evaporate To turn into a gas.

Expand To get bigger.

Firing Heating clay in a very hot oven, called a kiln, to make it extremely hard.

Fuse To join together by heating to a very high temperature; to melt together.

Glaze A shiny, glassy coating put on pottery to decorate and protect it. Glazes come in many different colours.

Hexagonal Six-sided.

Industrial Revolution The changes that took place in western Europe and the United States during the eighteenth and nineteenth centuries. Huge factories were built to produce goods in large amounts. Many people stopped working on farms and went to work in the new factories in the towns instead.

Kiln A hot oven used for heating clay to a very high temperature.

Kneading Working a mixture into a dough or paste by pressing and squeezing it.

Measurements The exact size of an object.

Minerals Chemicals, such as copper and iron, that are found in rocks.

Mould A hollow case into which a liquid, such as plaster, can be poured. When the plaster sets, it takes on the shape of the mould.

Particles The smallest specks of a substance.

Plaster A white substance that is soft when wet but becomes very hard when it dries out.

Potter's wheel A turntable which spins round. A potter puts a lump of soft clay in the middle and models the shape with his or her hands.

Sculpture A work of art made by carving or modelling.

Template A shape cut out of card. Templates are used to produce the same shape accurately several times.

Texture The feel of the surface of an object.

Three-dimensional Having depth as well as height and width.

Tomb A room, usually below ground, where a person is buried.

FURTHER INFORMATION

BOOKS TO READ

For children:
Dixon, Annabelle *Clay* (A & C Black, 1989)
Owen, Annie *The Models Book* (Franklin Watts, 1990)
Roussel, Mike *Clay* (Wayland, 1989)

For teachers:
Clay in the Classroom (Fulham Pottery and Inner London Education Authority, 1981)
Children and Clay (Fulham Pottery and Inner London Education Authority, 1981)

PLACES TO VISIT

Britain
The British Museum
Great Russell Street
London
WC1 3DG

Museum of London
London Wall
London
EC2Y 5HN

Victoria and Albert Museum
Cromwell Road
South Kensington
London
SW7 2RL

Gladstone Pottery Museum
Utoxeter Road
Longton
Stoke-on-Trent
Staffordshire
ST3 1PQ

Australia
Victoria State Craft
    Collection
Meat Market Craft Centre
Courtney Street North
Victoria 3051

Canada
Montreal Museum of Fine
    Arts
1379 Sherbrooke St West
Montreal
Quebec H3B 3E1

Royal Ontario Museum
100 Queen's Park
Toronto
Ontario
M5S 2C6

For further information about arts and crafts, contact the following organizations:

The Crafts Council
44A Pentonville Road
London
N1 9BY
UK

Crafts Council of New
    Zealand
22 The Terrace
Wellington
PO Box 498
Wellington Island
New Zealand

INDEX

ACKNOWLEDGEMENTS

The publishers would like to thank the following for allowing their photographs to be reproduced: Bridgeman Art Library 29 top left; Crafts Council 9 top right, 9 bottom right; C. M. Dixon 6 top and centre, 7 top left; Eye Ubiquitous 5 right (P. Seheult), 8 left (E. Hawkins), 9 left, 29 top right (P. Seheult), 29 centre right (C. Gibb); Gallery 10, Scottsdale and Santa Fe, USA 8 top right;

Michael Holford 7 bottom left, 28 left; Hutchison Library 8 bottom right (S. Errington); Tony Stone Worldwide 7 bottom right (J. Calder), 28 bottom right (D. Torckler); Werner Forman Archive 6 bottom, 7 top right; Zefa title page, 4, 28 top right, 29 centre left, 29 bottom left, 29 bottom right. All other photographs, including cover, were supplied by Zul Mukhida. Logo artwork by John Yates.

The work by Henry Moore, *Reclining Figure*, 1945, illustrated on page 29, has been reproduced by kind permission of the Henry Moore Foundation.

The publishers would like to thank William Blaik and Laura Green for allowing their work to appear in photographs on page 26. The pieces were made during a holiday workshop run by the Crafts Council.